IN THE YEAR 740 B.C., GOD APPEARED TO THE PROPHET ISAIAH IN A VISION.

WHOM SHALL I SEND AS MY MESSENGER TO FORETELL THE COMING OF MY SON?

LORD, HERE I AM; SEND ME.

ISAIAH PREACHED GOD'S MESSAGE TO THE PEOPLE.

THE LORD GOD SAYS THIS: "A VIRGIN WILL GIVE BIRTH TO A SON. HE WILL BE OUR KING. HE WILL BE CALLED 'EMMANUEL,' WHICH MEANS 'GOD IS WITH US'. HE WILL BE CALLED THE PRINCE OF PEACE."

PRAISE GOD, FOR THE SAVIOUR IS COMING!

FOR MANY YEARS, THE PEOPLE WAITED AND PRAYED FOR THEIR SAVIOUR. IN NAZARETH, A TOWN IN PALESTINE, A YOUNG MAIDEN WAS ALSO PRAYING. HER NAME WAS MARY.

MY SOUL IS THIRSTING FOR THE LORD. WHEN SHALL I SEE HIM FACE TO FACE?

SUDDENLY THE ROOM WAS FILLED WITH LIGHT.

HAIL MARY, FULL OF GRACE, THE LORD IS WITH YOU.

WHAT DOES HE MEAN?

FEAR NOT, MARY. I AM GABRIEL, THE MESSENGER OF GOD. YOU HAVE WON GOD'S FAVOUR. YOU SHALL HAVE A SON AND NAME HIM JESUS.

BUT HOW CAN THIS BE? I AM NOT MARRIED!

THE HOLY SPIRIT WILL COME ON YOU AND GOD'S POWER WILL REST ON YOU. FOR THIS REASON THE HOLY CHILD WILL BE CALLED THE SON OF GOD.

I AM THE LORD'S SERVANT. MAY HIS WILL BE DONE.

MARY WAS ENGAGED TO BE MARRIED TO JOSEPH, A CARPENTER OF NAZARETH.

MARY IS WITH CHILD? I WILL BREAK THE ENGAGEMENT QUIETLY.

4

THEN JOSEPH TOOK MARY TO HIS HOUSE.

AT THIS TIME, PALESTINE WAS OCCUPIED BY THE ROMANS. THEY IMPOSED THEIR LAWS, DEMANDED TAXES AND FORCED PEOPLE TO WORK FOR THEM.

TAKE THAT UP AT ONCE AND MOVE ON!

YOU LAZY FOOLS!

IN ADDITION, THE PEOPLE WERE TREATED CRUELLY BY THEIR OWN KING, HEROD, WHO WAS A HARSH TYRANT.

WHIP THEM AND THROW THEM IN THE DUNGEONS!

ONE DAY—

MARY, I HAVE BAD NEWS. THE ROMANS ARE TAKING A CENSUS. WE HAVE TO GO TO OUR HOMETOWN, BETHLEHEM, TO REGISTER OUR NAMES.

GOD MUST HAVE A PURPOSE IN THIS, JOSEPH. LET US GO.

BETHLEHEM WAS FAR AWAY FROM NAZARETH. AFTER MANY DAYS OF TRAVELLING—

I FEEL MY CHILD WILL BE BORN SOON. WILL WE REACH BETHLEHEM IN TIME?

WE ARE ALMOST THERE. I WILL TRY TO FIND A ROOM FOR YOU.

BETHLEHEM WAS FULL OF PEOPLE AND THERE WAS NO PLACE FOR THEM AT ANY INN.

TRY TO UNDERSTAND. MY WIFE IS IN A DELICATE CONDITION. ANY MOMENT....

SORRY, MY INN IS FULL.

NEVER MIND JOSEPH, GOD WILL LOOK AFTER US.

AS THEY CAME OUT OF THE TOWN—

MARY, LOOK! A STABLE! WE CAN STAY THERE FOR THE NIGHT.

PRAISED BE THE LORD FOR PROVIDING THIS SHELTER!

AT MIDNIGHT, THE CHILD WAS BORN.

WHAT A LOVELY CHILD—MY LITTLE SON, JESUS, THE HOPE OF ISRAEL!

WHEN THE ANGELS HAD GONE, THE SHEPHERDS WENT TO THE STABLE.

THIS CHILD IS DESTINED FOR GREAT THINGS!

HOW HAPPY WE ARE TO BEHOLD HIM WITH OUR OWN EYES!

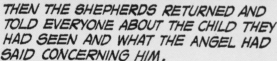

THEN THE SHEPHERDS RETURNED AND TOLD EVERYONE ABOUT THE CHILD THEY HAD SEEN AND WHAT THE ANGEL HAD SAID CONCERNING HIM.

ON THE SAME NIGHT, THREE WISE MEN FROM THE EAST CAME TOWARDS JERUSALEM, GUIDED BY A BRILLIANT STAR.

THEY STOPPED AT JERUSALEM.

KING HEROD RULES HERE LET US ASK HIM ABOUT THE NEW KING.

IN THE COURT OF KING HEROD—

PEACE BE WITH YOU, KING HEROD!

WHAT IS THE PURPOSE OF YOUR VISIT, MY FRIENDS?

WE ARE LOOKING FOR THE KING OF THE JEWS WHO HAS JUST BEEN BORN.

WE HAVE FOLLOWED HIS STAR AND HAVE COME TO WORSHIP HIM.

MY PRIESTS WILL SEE IF THIS IS WRITTEN IN THE HOLY BOOKS.

THE SACRED TEXT SAYS THAT THE KING OF ISRAEL SHALL BE BORN AT BETHLEHEM.

GO TO BETHLEHEM AND LOOK FOR HIM. THEN COME BACK AND REPORT TO ME, SO THAT I, TOO, CAN WORSHIP HIM!

WHEN THE WISE MEN LEFT JERUSALEM, THEY SAW THE STAR AGAIN WHICH LED THEM TO THE STABLE AT BETHLEHEM.

I BRING YOU A GIFT OF GOLD, FOR YOU ARE THE KING OF ALL NATIONS.

FROM ME, A GIFT OF INCENSE, FOR YOU ARE THE SON OF GOD.

AND I BRING A GIFT OF MYRRH TO EMBALM YOUR BODY— FOR YOU WILL DIE TO SAVE US.

IN WELCOMING THE SAVIOUR THE WISE MEN REPRESENTED ALL MEN OF GOOD WILL. BUT THE POWERS OF EVIL WERE ALSO AT WORK.

SO DURING THE NIGHT, AN ANGEL APPEARED TO THE WISE MEN.

LEAVE BY ANOTHER ROUTE. DO NOT GO BACK TO HEROD. HE WANTS TO KILL THE CHILD.

THE WISE MEN OBEYED THE ANGEL.

MEANWHILE, HEROD WAS GETTING RESTLESS. JUST THEN—

YOUR MAJESTY! THE THREE WISE MEN HAVE LEFT THE COUNTRY!

I MUST ACT QUICKLY! BUT I DO NOT KNOW WHERE THE CHILD IS. HE MAY ESCAPE!

HEROD GAVE A CRUEL ORDER TO HIS GENERAL.

GO WITH TWO HUNDRED SOLDIERS AND KILL ALL BOYS BELOW TWO YEARS OF AGE IN AND AROUND BETHLEHEM!

MEANWHILE, IN BETHLEHEM, AN ANGEL APPEARED TO JOSEPH.

JOSEPH! TAKE THE CHILD AND FLEE TO EGYPT. HEROD IS OUT TO KILL HIM.

JOSEPH AND MARY OBEYED THE ANGEL AND LEFT BETHLEHEM

CAN'T WE REST FOR A SHORT WHILE? WE HAVE BEEN TRAVELLING FOR HOURS!

NO, MY DEAR MARY. WE MUST TAKE THE CHILD OUT OF KING HEROD'S REACH.

SOON HEROD'S SOLDIERS REACHED BETHLEHEM.

KILL ALL OF THEM! NOT A SINGLE ONE WILL ESCAPE!

A SLAUGHTER OF INNOCENT AND HELPLESS CHILDREN! DARK DAYS ARE UPON US!

SPARE MY CHILD!

HAVE MERCY! HE IS MY FIRST BORN!

BUT THE CHILD THEY WANTED TO DESTROY WAS SAFE IN EGYPT IN THE LOVING CARE OF JOSEPH AND MARY.

MARY, WE WILL STAY HERE IN EGYPT UNTIL THE LORD TELLS US TO RETURN.

SOME TIME LATER, WHEN HEROD WAS DEAD, THE ANGEL APPEARED AGAIN TO JOSEPH.

KING HEROD IS DEAD. IT IS NOW SAFE TO RETURN.

SO MARY AND JOSEPH RETURNED TO NAZARETH.

AT LAST, WE ARE BACK HOME!

JESUS GREW UP TO BE A STUDIOUS AND OBEDIENT BOY.

JESUS, I NEED SOME FIREWOOD. COULD YOU GO AND GET SOME?

YES, MOTHER.

JESUS LEARNT HOW TO READ AND WRITE. HE STARTED READING THE HOLY BIBLE.

IN—THE—BEGIN—NING GOD—MADE—HEA—VEN AND EARTH....

EVERY DAY HE READ THE SACRED TEXT AND MEDITATED ON IT.

HE CAN SIT LIKE THAT FOR HOURS. SURELY, HE IS TALKING TO HIS HEAVENLY FATHER?

WHEN JESUS WAS TWELVE YEARS OLD, HE WAS TAKEN BY HIS PARENTS TO JERUSALEM TO CELEBRATE THE ANNUAL FEAST IN THE TEMPLE.*

FATHER, I AM LOOKING FORWARD SO MUCH TO SEEING THE TEMPLE.

YOU WILL LIKE IT, SON. IT IS THE MOST SACRED PLACE IN OUR COUNTRY.

* AT THE AGE OF TWELVE A JEWISH BOY WAS CONSIDERED AN ADULT

17

WE ADORE YOU! WE PRAISE YOU! WE WORSHIP YOU!

ON THE WAY BACK HOME AFTER THE FEAST—

JOSEPH, ISN'T JESUS WITH YOU AND THE OTHER MEN?

NO, MARY I THOUGHT HE WAS WITH YOU! LET US GO BACK TO THE TEMPLE TO LOOK FOR HIM.

JOSEPH AND MARY RETURNED TO THE TEMPLE AND FOUND HIM DEEP IN DISCUSSION IN THE TEMPLE.

THIS BOY IS UNUSUALLY WISE.

MY SON, HOW COULD YOU DO THIS TO US? WE THOUGHT YOU WERE LOST!

MOTHER, DIDN'T YOU KNOW I HAD TO BE HERE IN THE HOUSE OF GOD, MY FATHER?

AS A TEENAGER JESUS WENT REGULARLY TO THE SYNAGOGUE* TO PRAY AND TO LISTEN TO THE READING OF THE HOLY BOOKS.

FATHER IN HEAVEN, LET ME KNOW WHEN IT IS TIME FOR ME TO BEGIN MY MISSION.

*JEWISH PRAYER HOUSE

WHEN HE GREW UP TO BE A YOUNG MAN, JESUS WORKED AS A CARPENTER, MAKING TOOLS AND BUILDING HOUSES.

LIKE HIS FATHER, JOSEPH, JESUS IS A FIRST-RATE CARPENTER.

YES, I WILL ASK HIM TO BUILD MY NEW HOUSE FOR ME.

IF ONLY PEOPLE KNEW THAT I HAVE COME TO BUILD A NEW WORLD OF LOVE AND PEACE!

WHEN JESUS WAS THIRTY YEARS OLD, AN ASCETIC CALLED JOHN THE BAPTIST BEGAN TO PREACH NEAR THE RIVER JORDAN.

PREPARE THE WAY FOR THE LORD IN YOUR HEARTS! CHANGE YOUR SINFUL WAYS! RECEIVE BAPTISM* IN WATER AS A SIGN OF YOUR NEW LIFE!

* A RITE IN WHICH A PERSON IS IMMERSED IN WATER TO SYMBOLIZE A CHANGE FROM HIS SINFUL LIFE

LARGE NUMBERS OF PEOPLE WENT TO JOHN TO BE BAPTISED. ONE DAY, JESUS WENT TO HIM.

JOHN, ARE YOU THE PROMISED SAVIOUR?

NO, I BAPTISE ONLY WITH WATER BUT IN YOUR MIDST IS THE SAVIOUR WHO WILL BAPTISE YOU WITH GOD'S HOLY SPIRIT HE IS MUCH GREATER THAN I AM I AM NOT WORTHY TO UNTIE THE STRAPS OF HIS SANDALS.

JESUS STEPPED FORWARD.

PLEASE BAPTISE ME TOO!

JOHN BAPTISED JESUS.

THIS IS MY BELOVED SON IN WHOM I AM WELL PLEASED.

GOD THE FATHER DECLARED JESUS TO BE HIS SON, AND GOD'S SPIRIT CAME DOWN UPON HIM IN THE SHAPE OF A DOVE.

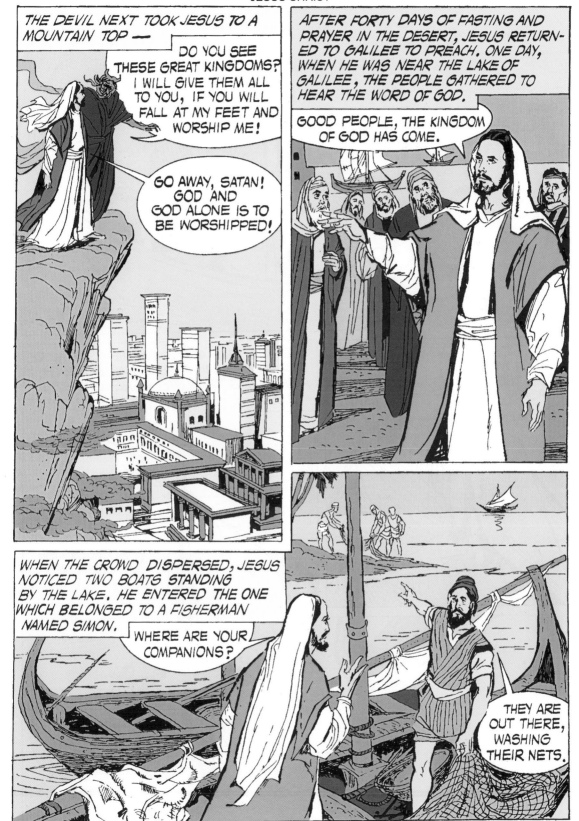

THE DEVIL NEXT TOOK JESUS TO A MOUNTAIN TOP —

DO YOU SEE THESE GREAT KINGDOMS? I WILL GIVE THEM ALL TO YOU, IF YOU WILL FALL AT MY FEET AND WORSHIP ME!

GO AWAY, SATAN! GOD AND GOD ALONE IS TO BE WORSHIPPED!

AFTER FORTY DAYS OF FASTING AND PRAYER IN THE DESERT, JESUS RETURNED TO GALILEE TO PREACH. ONE DAY, WHEN HE WAS NEAR THE LAKE OF GALILEE, THE PEOPLE GATHERED TO HEAR THE WORD OF GOD.

GOOD PEOPLE, THE KINGDOM OF GOD HAS COME.

WHEN THE CROWD DISPERSED, JESUS NOTICED TWO BOATS STANDING BY THE LAKE. HE ENTERED THE ONE WHICH BELONGED TO A FISHERMAN NAMED SIMON.

WHERE ARE YOUR COMPANIONS?

THEY ARE OUT THERE, WASHING THEIR NETS.

SIMON WAS ASTONISHED AND FRIGHTENED—

LEAVE ME, LORD YOU ARE THE SON OF GOD AND I AM A SINFUL MAN!

SIMON PETER, DO NOT BE AFRAID FROM NOW ON, YOU WILL BE A FISHER OF MEN!

JESUS CALLED SIMON AND OTHERS TO BE HIS FIRST DISCIPLES.

COME, FOLLOW ME, SIMON AND YOU, TOO, ANDREW, JAMES AND JOHN.

AMONG THEM WAS MATTHEW, WHO COLLECTED TAXES FOR THE ROMANS. THE JEWS HATED TAX COLLECTORS.

MATTHEW, LEAVE YOUR MONEY AND FOLLOW ME

YES, MASTER.

JESUS CHOSE TWELVE FROM AMONG HIS DISCIPLES.

YOU ARE MY APOSTLES AND YOU WILL PREACH THE GOOD NEWS OF GOD'S LOVE FOR MEN. IN MY NAME YOU WILL WORK MANY WONDERS.

ONE DAY, JESUS CAME TO A TOWN CALLED NAIN—

LOOK, MASTER! A FUNERAL!

DO NOT WEEP. TELL ME YOUR TROUBLES.

I AM A WIDOW— AND NOW MY ONLY SON IS DEAD!

AS MORE AND MORE POOR AND SUFFERING PEOPLE CAME TO JESUS, HE BEGAN TO SHOW THEM THE PATH TO TRUE HAPPINESS.

"HAPPY ARE THE POOR: FOR GOD'S KINGDOM BELONGS TO THEM."

"HAPPY ARE THE MERCIFUL: FOR GOD WILL SHOW THEM MERCY."

"HAPPY ARE THOSE WHO HUNGER AND THIRST FOR JUSTICE: FOR GOD WILL BRING THEM JUSTICE."

"HAPPY ARE THE PURE OF HEART: FOR THEY SHALL SEE GOD."

BE COMPASSIONATE DO NOT CONDEMN ANYONE AND YOU WILL NOT BE CONDEMNED FORGIVE AND YOU WILL BE FORGIVEN. GIVE TO OTHERS, JUST AS GOD GIVES TO YOU.

JESUS OFTEN SPENT WHOLE NIGHTS IN PRAYER.

ONE DAY—

MASTER, TEACH US ALSO TO PRAY.

PRAY TO GOD THUS: OUR FATHER IN HEAVEN, HOLY BE YOUR NAME. MAY YOUR KINGDOM COME AND YOUR WILL BE DONE. GIVE US THIS DAY OUR DAILY BREAD FORGIVE OUR SINS AS WE FORGIVE THOSE WHO SIN AGAINST US.

WHEN YOU PRAY, SAY LITTLE — BUT PRAY WITH ALL YOUR HEART. WHEN YOU PRAY, DO NOT PRAY JUST TO MAKE A SHOW OF YOURSELF. YOUR FATHER IN HEAVEN LISTENS TO YOU IN SECRET!

EVEN THE ROMANS MARVELLED AT THE TEACHINGS OF JESUS AND HIS MIRACLES. ONE DAY, A ROMAN OFFICIAL CAME TO HIM.

MY SERVANT IS PARALYSED. HE IS DYING! PLEASE CURE HIM.

I WILL COME TO YOUR HOUSE AT ONCE.

LORD, I AM NOT WORTHY THAT YOU SHOULD COME UNDER MY ROOF JUST GIVE THE ORDER FROM HERE AND HE WILL BE CURED.

NOWHERE HAVE I FOUND FAITH LIKE THIS — NOT EVEN AMONG MY OWN PEOPLE.

GO HOME. YOUR SERVANT IS HEALED.

WHEN THE ROMAN OFFICIAL RETURNED HOME—

SIR, YOUR SERVANT IS WELL AGAIN!

I KNEW IT! I KNEW IT!

JESUS WENT TO THE SAMARITANS, TOO, EVEN THOUGH THEY WERE DISLIKED BY THE JEWS.

GIVE ME SOME WATER TO DRINK.

YOU ARE A JEW. YET YOU ASK ME, A SAMARITAN FOR WATER?

IF YOU KNEW WHO I WAS, YOU WOULD HAVE ASKED ME FOR LIFE-GIVING WATER SO THAT YOU WOULD NEVER BE THIRSTY AGAIN.

SIR, GIVE ME THAT LIFE-GIVING WATER.

FIRST, GO AND CALL YOUR HUSBAND.

I HAVE NO HUSBAND, SIR.

YOU HAVE HAD FIVE HUSBANDS. THE MAN YOU ARE LIVING WITH NOW IS NOT YOUR HUSBAND.

YOU SPEAK LIKE A PROPHET— LIKE THE SAVIOUR WHO IS TO COME.

I AM HE.

THE WOMAN WENT AND TOLD HER NEIGHBOURS ABOUT JESUS.

COME AND SEE THE MAN WHO SAW RIGHT INTO MY PAST LIFE. SURELY HE IS THE PROMISED SAVIOUR!

JESUS WELCOMED THE CROWDS THAT CAME TO HIM.

COME TO ME ALL YOU WHO ARE TIRED AND OVER-BURDENED AND I WILL GIVE YOU REST.

"... WHO LEFT HIM WOUNDED AND HALF DEAD.

"NOW A PRIEST PASSED BY BUT HE DID NOT CARE.

HELP!

"HE JUST IGNORED HIM.

H··E··L··P

"BUT A SAMARITAN TRAVELLER HAD COMPASSION ON HIM. HE CLEANED HIS WOUNDS AND BANDAGED THEM.

"THE SAMARITAN PUT THE MAN ON HIS DONKEY···

"··· AND CARRIED HIM TO AN INN."

SIR, PLEASE LOOK AFTER HIM UNTIL MY RETURN. I WILL PAY ALL THE EXPENSES.

NOW TELL ME WHICH OF THESE MEN SHOWED BROTHERLY LOVE?

THE MAN WHO SHOWED MERCY.

THE GOOD SAMARITAN.

GO AND DO THE SAME. LOVE YOUR NEIGHBOUR AS YOURSELF.

WHO DOES HE THINK HE IS? IS HE TRYING TO SAY THAT THOUGH WE, THE PHARISEES, ARE THE PRIESTS AND LEADERS OF THE JEWS, WE ARE WORSE THAN SINNERS AND SAMARITANS?

THAT IS CERTAINLY HIS MEANING HE ALWAYS SPEAKS AGAINST US!

JESUS WENT ON TEACHING—

ON THE DAY OF JUDGEMENT, AT THE END OF THE WORLD, WHEN ALL THE DEAD WILL RISE, I WILL COME AGAIN AS THE GLORIOUS KING OF THE WHOLE WORLD.

JESUS WENT ON PREACHING—

DON'T BE LIKE THE PHARISEES. THEY LIKE TO SHOW OFF. OUTSIDE THEY LOOK SO HOLY, BUT INSIDE THEY ARE CORRUPT.

ONCE, TWO MEN WENT TO PRAY IN THE TEMPLE: A PHARISEE AND A TAX COLLECTOR.

GOD, I THANK YOU THAT I AM NOT GREEDY AND DISHONEST LIKE THE TAX COLLECTOR OVER THERE. I FAST TWICE A WEEK. I GIVE MONEY TO THE POOR.

PLEASE, GOD, HAVE MERCY ON ME — A POOR SINNER.

GOD WAS SURELY PLEASED WITH THE HUMBLE SINNER, AND NOT WITH THE PROUD PHARISEE. HE WHO MAKES HIMSELF GREAT WILL BE HUMBLED AND HE WHO HUMBLES HIMSELF WILL BE MADE GREAT.

AGAIN HE IS INSULTING US. HE IS GOING TOO FAR!

THE PHARISEES TRIED TO FIND FAULT WITH JESUS.

WHY DO YOU EAT WITH SINNERS?

I HAVE COME TO SAVE THOSE WHO ARE LOST. IT IS NOT THE HEALTHY WHO NEED A DOCTOR BUT THE SICK.

WHAT DOES HE MEAN, JOHN?

PETER, I THINK THE TEMPLE MEANS HIS OWN BODY.

JESUS EXPLAINED THE MEANING OF HIS WORDS TO HIS DISCIPLES.

THE TIME WILL COME WHEN THEY WILL CONDEMN ME TO DEATH THEY WILL CRUCIFY ME AND BURY ME BUT AFTER THREE DAYS I WILL RISE FROM THE GRAVE.

THE CHIEF PRIESTS OF THE TEMPLE WERE FURIOUS WITH JESUS.

ANYONE WHO SAYS THAT JESUS IS THE SAVIOUR WILL NOT BE ALLOWED TO ENTER THE TEMPLE.

THE PRIESTS' ORDERS MADE PEOPLE AFRAID BUT SOME BRAVELY KEPT GOING TO JESUS—

LORD, HAVE MERCY ON ME, A POOR BLIND MAN.

MASTER, THIS MAN, JACOB, WAS BORN BLIND HE HAS BEEN BEGGING FOR MANY YEARS.

JESUS SPAT ON THE GROUND, MADE SOME PASTE AND APPLIED IT TO THE BLIND MAN'S EYES.

JACOB, YOU WILL SOON SEE THE GLORY OF GOD! FOR I AM THE LIGHT OF THE WORLD.

NOW GO AND WASH YOUR EYES IN THE POOL OF SILOAM.

LATER—

I CAN SEE! I CAN SEE!

WHEN THE PHARISEES HEARD ABOUT THE MIRACLE, THEY TRIED TO FIND FAULT WITH JESUS.

HE CURED YOU ON A SABBATH DAY! WE ARE NOT ALLOWED TO DO ANYTHING BUT PRAY AND REST ON THE SABBATH! THAT MAN, JESUS, IS A SINNER!

JESUS IS A SINNER? CAN A SINNER OPEN THE EYES OF A MAN WHO WAS BORN BLIND!

THEY TOOK THE WOMAN TO JESUS.

MASTER, THIS WOMAN WAS CAUGHT IN ADULTERY. THE LAW SAYS SHE MUST BE STONED TO DEATH.

WHAT DO YOU SAY?

JESUS SAID NOTHING. HE STOOPED DOWN AND WITH HIS FINGER WROTE ON THE GROUND.

SHAMELESS WOMAN!

STONE HER TO DEATH!

SPEAK UP MASTER! WHY ARE YOU SILENT?

IS THERE ANYONE HERE WHO HAS NOT SINNED A SINGLE TIME? THEN LET HIM BE THE FIRST TO CAST A STONE AT HER!

THUS REMINDED OF THEIR OWN MISDEEDS THE PHARISEES BEGAN TO LEAVE ONE BY ONE.

TAKE THE TEMPLE GUARDS WITH YOU AND ARREST HIM.

ON THE NEXT DAY, WHEN THE TEMPLE GUARDS WENT TO ARREST JESUS, THEY FOUND HIM PREACHING.

I AM THE GOOD SHEPHERD. THE GOOD SHEPHERD LAYS DOWN HIS LIFE FOR HIS SHEEP.

GO ON! ARREST HIM!

HOW CAN WE ARREST A MAN WHO IS READY TO DIE FOR US?

AND THE GUARDS LEFT WITHOUT DISTURBING JESUS.

LATER—

WHAT HAPPENED? WHY DIDN'T YOU ARREST HIM?

MY LORD, I HAVE NOT HEARD ANY MAN SPEAK LIKE HIM IN ALL MY LIFE!

WHAT! HE HAS FOOLED YOU TOO?

MY LORD, THEY ARE ALL AFRAID OF THE CROWD.

HM..M. THEN WE MUST FIND A BETTER WAY TO GET RID OF HIM! KEEP A CLOSE WATCH ON HIS DISCIPLES — SPECIALLY ON JUDAS.

THE PHARISEES FOLLOWED JESUS WHEREVER HE WENT. NOW JESUS HAD THREE CLOSE FRIENDS: LAZARUS AND HIS SISTERS, MARTHA AND MARY. HEARING THAT LAZARUS WAS VERY ILL, JESUS WENT TO THE VILLAGE OF BETHANY, TO VISIT HIM.

WHEN JESUS ARRIVED NEAR BETHANY, MARTHA CAME OUT TO MEET HIM.

LORD, MY BROTHER HAS DIED! IF YOU HAD BEEN HERE THIS WOULD NOT HAVE HAPPENED.

DON'T CRY, MARTHA. YOUR BROTHER WILL RISE AGAIN!.

I KNOW HE WILL RISE AGAIN ON THE LAST DAY WHEN THIS WORLD ENDS.

I HAVE COME TO GIVE NEW LIFE TO ALL MEN. HE WHO BELIEVES IN ME WILL NEVER DIE. DO YOU BELIEVE THIS, MARTHA?

YES, LORD. I BELIEVE YOU ARE THE SON OF GOD!

JESUS THEN MET MARY, THE OTHER SISTER OF LAZARUS.

MARY! WIPE AWAY YOUR TEARS! SHOW ME WHERE LAZARUS LIES.

LORD, COME AND SEE.

HE IS WEEPING! SEE HOW MUCH HE LOVED LAZARUS!

THAT PERFUME MUST HAVE COST A FORTUNE!

THE TWO PHARISEES WERE PRESENT, SPYING ON JESUS.

THAT'S THE DISCIPLE, JUDAS— THE ONE IN CHARGE OF THEIR COMMON FUND.

I HEAR HE QUIETLY POCKETS MOST OF THEIR MONEY.

WHAT A WASTE! MASTER, WE COULD HAVE SOLD THIS PERFUME FOR 300 SILVER COINS AND GIVEN THE MONEY TO THE POOR!

JESUS TURNED TO JUDAS.

THE POOR ARE ALWAYS WITH YOU. BUT I WON'T BE WITH YOU FOR LONG. MARY HAS ANOINTED ME TO PREPARE ME FOR MY DEATH AND BURIAL.

HE HAS INSULTED ME! I WILL MAKE HIM PAY FOR IT!

THAT NIGHT, JUDAS MET THE TWO SPIES.

TAKE ME TO THE TEMPLE HIGH PRIEST. I CAN HELP YOU ARREST JESUS.

AHA! THAT'S JUST WHAT WE WANT!

THE NEXT DAY, JESUS LEFT BETHANY AND WENT TO JERUSALEM. THE NEWS OF HIS RECENT MIRACLE HAD SPREAD AND CROWDS FOLLOWED HIM EVERYWHERE.

* SAVE US

WE MUST ACT FAST! HE IS BECOMING TOO POPULAR!

THEY HAVE ALL HEARD ABOUT LAZARUS!

LIKE OTHER JEWS IN JERUSALEM, JESUS AND HIS TWELVE DISCIPLES CELEBRATED THE PASSOVER WITH A SPECIAL SUPPER.

I HAVE LONGED TO EAT THIS LAST SUPPER* WITH YOU BEFORE I LEAVE YOU FOREVER.

WHY DOES JESUS WISH TO LEAVE US?

I DON'T UNDERSTAND THAT EITHER!

BEFORE BEGINNING THE MEAL—

LORD, ARE YOU GOING TO WASH OUR FEET? THAT IS THE DUTY OF SERVANTS!

* THIS EPISODE LATER CAME TO BE KNOWN AS THE "LAST SUPPER"

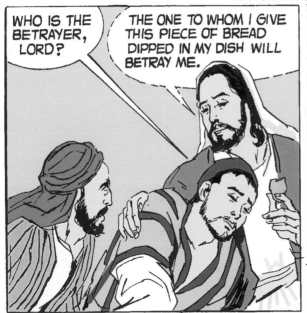

AS THEY WERE EATING, JESUS TOOK SOME BREAD, BLESSED IT, AND GAVE IT TO HIS DISCIPLES.

THIS IS MY BODY, BROKEN AND OFFERED UP FOR YOU.

I AM THE BREAD OF LIFE. MY FLESH IS REAL FOOD AND MY BLOOD IS REAL LIFE-GIVING DRINK!

HE THEN TOOK A CUP OF WINE, GAVE THANKS TO GOD, AND OFFERED IT TO HIS DISCIPLES, ONE BY ONE.

DRINK THIS— FOR THIS IS MY BLOOD, WHICH WILL BE SHED FOR YOU AND FOR ALL MEN, FOR THE FORGIVENESS OF THEIR SINS.

EVERY TIME YOU COME TOGETHER IN MY NAME, DO AS I HAVE DONE, UNTIL I COME AGAIN.

AS THE LAST SUPPER ENDED—

DON'T BE SAD! I WON'T LEAVE YOU HELPLESS. I WILL SEND THE HOLY SPIRIT TO HELP YOU. PEACE BE WITH YOU!

MY TIME HAS COME. LET US GO OUT.

WHAT WAS FORETOLD ABOUT ME IN THE HOLY WRITINGS WILL SOON COME TRUE: "GOD PLACED THE BURDEN OF OUR SINS ON HIM. LIKE A LAMB THAT IS LED TO THE SLAUGHTER-HOUSE, HE NEVER OPENED HIS MOUTH."

THEN JESUS WENT TO AN OLIVE GROVE CALLED GETHSEMANE, OUTSIDE JERUSALEM.

PETER, JAMES AND JOHN, STAY HERE NEAR ME AND PRAY.

JESUS PRAYED.

MY FATHER, EVERYTHING IS POSSIBLE FOR YOU. TAKE THIS BITTER SUFFERING AWAY FROM ME!

AS HE PRAYED, HE SWEATED BLOOD.

BUT LET **YOUR** WILL BE DONE, NOT MINE!

WHEN HE AROSE FROM PRAYER, HE FOUND HIS DISCIPLES SLEEPING.

COULD YOU NOT KEEP AWAKE AND PRAY WITH ME? WAKE UP NOW!

JUST THEN, JUDAS APPEARED WITH A BAND OF GUARDS.

JESUS WAS TAKEN TO JERUSALEM.

JOHN, THEY ARE TAKING HIM TO CAIAPHAS!

LET'S FOLLOW THEM, PETER.

JESUS WAS BROUGHT BEFORE CAIAPHAS.

IN THE NAME OF GOD, I ASK YOU: ARE YOU THE SON OF GOD?

I AM. AND I WILL COME AGAIN ON THE CLOUDS OF HEAVEN AS THE KING OF KINGS.

BLASPHEMY! HE CLAIMS TO BE THE EQUAL OF GOD!

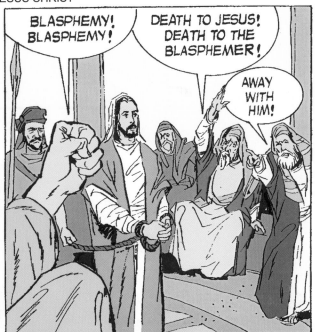

BLASPHEMY! BLASPHEMY!

DEATH TO JESUS! DEATH TO THE BLASPHEMER!

AWAY WITH HIM!

MEANWHILE PETER WAS SITTING OUTSIDE THE PALACE OF CAIAPHAS—

YOU, TOO, WERE WITH JESUS, WEREN'T YOU?

HUH? I DON'T KNOW WHAT YOU ARE TALKING ABOUT!

HEY! BUT YOU SOUND LIKE A GALILEAN!

I TELL YOU I DON'T KNOW THIS JESUS!

YOU ARE THE SAME MAN WHO STRUCK AT MY BROTHER'S EAR. I'LL SHOW YOU!

GOD IS MY WITNESS, I AM NOT THE MAN!

JUST THEN A COCK CREW.

PETER REMEMBERED WHAT JESUS HAD PROPHESIED—

I DENIED HIM THRICE — JUST AS HE HAD WARNED ME.

JESUS LOOKED AT PETER.

THAT NIGHT IN THE PRISON—

AHA! MIGHTY PROPHET! TELL US NOW WHO HIT YOU?

WHEN MORNING CAME, THEY TOOK JESUS TO PILATE, THE ROMAN GOVERNOR.

YOUR EXCELLENCY, THIS MAN IS DANGEROUS TO THE ROMAN EMPIRE. HE IS PREACHING REVOLUTION TO THE CROWDS! HE SAYS HE IS THE KING OF KINGS!

WE HAVE NO POWER TO SENTENCE ANYONE TO DEATH. SO WE HAVE BROUGHT HIM TO YOU.

WHAT IS THEIR GAME? I THINK THEY ARE USING ME TO GET RID OF HIM. YET THERE IS NOT MUCH I CAN DO TO SAVE HIM.

PILATE QUESTIONED JESUS—

SPEAK UP. ARE YOU A KING?

YES.

HE IS SO SILENT, SO CALM.

JESUS MEANT THAT HE WAS A KING— BUT NOT OF THE WORLDLY KINGDOM PILATE UNDERSTOOD THIS AND WISHED TO SAVE HIM.

HE ADDRESSED THE CROWDS OUTSIDE.

PEOPLE OF JERUSALEM! EVERY YEAR I RELEASE ONE PRISONER AT YOUR PASSOVER FEAST I HAVE TWO PRISONERS RIGHT HERE BARABBAS WHO IS A NOTORIOUS CRIMINAL AND JESUS, WHO HAS COMMITTED NO CRIME NOW, SHALL I SET JESUS FREE?

BUT THE CROWDS, PROMPTED BY THE CHIEF PRIESTS, SHOUTED—

NO! RELEASE BARABBAS!

AWAY WITH JESUS!

BUT WHAT SHALL I DO WITH JESUS, THE KING OF THE JEWS?

CRUCIFY HIM! CRUCIFY HIM!

WE HAVE NO KING BUT CAESAR!

YOUR EXCELLENCY, IF YOU SPARE THIS MAN, YOU WILL BE ACTING AGAINST THE EMPEROR!

THERE WILL BE RIOTS IN JERUSALEM!

PILATE TRIED ANOTHER WAY OF SAVING JESUS —

CENTURION,* SCOURGE JESUS.

SO JESUS WAS SCOURGED.

THE SOLDIERS THEN MOCKED JESUS —

HAIL! KING OF THE JEWS!

LET'S GIVE THE KING A CROWN OF THORNS!

JESUS REMAINED SILENT.

JESUS WAS THEN BROUGHT BEFORE THE CROWD TO SEE IF THEY WOULD BE MOVED BY PITY.

BEHOLD THE MAN!

* OFFICER IN CHARGE OF A HUNDRED SOLDIERS

BUT THEY SHOUTED LOUDER STILL.

CRUCIFY HIM!

CRUCIFY HIM!

PILATE FAILED TO SAVE JESUS. HE WASHED HIS HANDS RITUALLY IN FRONT OF ALL.

DON'T BLAME ME FOR SHEDDING THE BLOOD OF THIS INNOCENT MAN!

MAY HIS BLOOD BE UPON OUR HEADS!

CENTURION, RELEASE BARABBAS AND CRUCIFY JESUS!

SO BARABBAS, THE KILLER, WAS SAVED, AND JESUS, THE SAVIOUR, WAS LED AWAY TO BE KILLED ON A CROSS.

JESUS CARRIED THE HEAVY CROSS TO A HILL CALLED CALVARY. TWO THIEVES, WHO WERE ALSO SENTENCED TO DEATH, WERE TAKEN WITH HIM.

ON THE WAY, JESUS SAW SOME WOMEN CRYING.

DON'T WEEP FOR ME. WEEP FOR YOURSELVES AND FOR YOUR CHILDREN.

JESUS MET HIS MOTHER, MARY.

THE CROSS WAS SO HEAVY THAT JESUS FELL UNDER ITS WEIGHT MANY TIMES BEFORE HE REACHED CALVARY.

THE SOLDIERS THEN STRIPPED JESUS AND NAILED HIM TO THE CROSS. TWO THIEVES WERE ALSO CRUCIFIED ON EITHER SIDE OF JESUS.

HE SAVED OTHERS, BUT HE CANNOT SAVE HIMSELF!

IF YOU ARE THE SON OF GOD, COME DOWN FROM THE CROSS!

THOUGH THEY MOCKED HIM WHILE HE WAS DYING, HE FORGAVE THEM ALL. HE PRAYED FOR THEM.

FATHER, FORGIVE THEM. THEY DO NOT KNOW WHAT THEY ARE DOING.

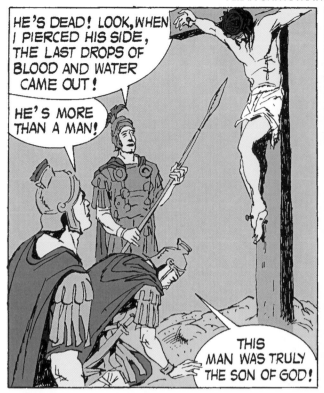

HE'S DEAD! LOOK, WHEN I PIERCED HIS SIDE, THE LAST DROPS OF BLOOD AND WATER CAME OUT!

HE'S MORE THAN A MAN!

THIS MAN WAS TRULY THE SON OF GOD!

LATER, THEY TOOK DOWN THE BODY FROM THE CROSS···

···AND THEY LAID JESUS IN THE TOMB.

THAT EVENING AT THE COURT OF THE GOVERNOR, PILATE—

YOUR EXCELLENCY, GIVE US GUARDS TO PROTECT THE TOMB OF JESUS. HE SAID HE WOULD RISE AGAIN IN THREE DAYS...

···AND HIS DISCIPLES MAY STEAL HIS BODY AND THEN TELL THE PEOPLE THAT HE HAS RISEN FROM THE DEAD!

AT SUNRISE, JESUS ROSE FROM THE TOMB. HE WAS ALIVE AGAIN.

THE DAY ON WHICH CHRIST AROSE AGAIN IS CELEBRATED EVERY YEAR AND IS CALLED EASTER SUNDAY.

THE SOLDIERS RUSHED TO CAIAPHAS, AND TOLD HIM WHAT HAD HAPPENED.

NOW, NOW, CALM DOWN! SPEAK TO NO ONE OF WHAT YOU HAVE SEEN!

HERE'S FIVE HUNDRED SILVER PIECES FOR EACH ONE OF YOU!

HA! HA! JUST SPREAD AROUND THE STORY THAT THE DISCIPLES STOLE HIS BODY!

MEANWHILE, MARY MAGDELENE A FOLLOWER OF JESUS, CAME TO THE TOMB.

THE STONE HAS BEEN ROLLED AWAY! THE TOMB IS EMPTY! WHERE HAVE THEY TAKEN MY LORD?

SHE RAN BACK TO THE CITY—

PETER, JOHN— THE TOMB IS EMPTY!

LET'S GO AND SEE! HURRY UP!

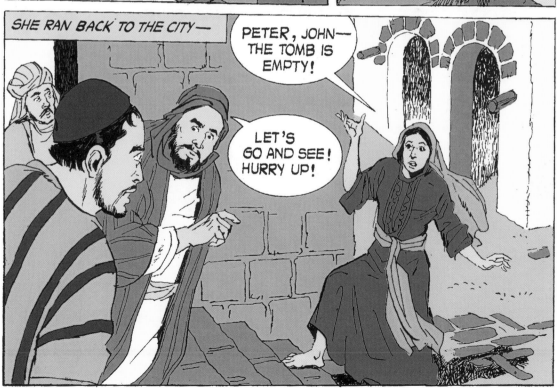

MARY!

OH! JESUS, MY LORD!

THAT SAME EVENING, AS HIS DISCIPLES WERE RETURNING HOME FROM JERUSALEM, JESUS JOINED THEM.

WHY ARE YOU SO SAD?

BUT THEY FAILED TO RECOGNIZE JESUS.

JESUS HAD TOLD US HE WOULD RISE AGAIN AFTER THREE DAYS. THREE DAYS HAVE NOW PASSED BUT THERE IS NO SIGN OF HIM YET.

NO SIGN OF HIM? HOW FOOLISH YOU ARE! WASN'T IT NECESSARY FOR HIM TO DIE LIKE A LAMB AND SHED BLOOD TO SAVE ALL MEN FROM SIN? WASN'T IT FORETOLD BY THE PROPHETS?

HOW CAN A DEAD MAN COME BACK TO LIFE? UNLESS I PUT MY FINGER ON THE WOUNDS IN HIS HANDS, I WILL NOT BELIEVE!

EIGHT DAYS LATER, JESUS CAME—

PEACE BE WITH YOU, THOMAS!

TAKE MY HANDS AND FEEL THE WOUNDS. YOU NEED PROOF, MY DOUBTING THOMAS!

MY LORD AND MY GOD!

THOMAS, YOU SEE WITH YOUR EYES AND THEN BELIEVE. HAPPY ARE THOSE WHO DON'T SEE AND YET BELIEVE.

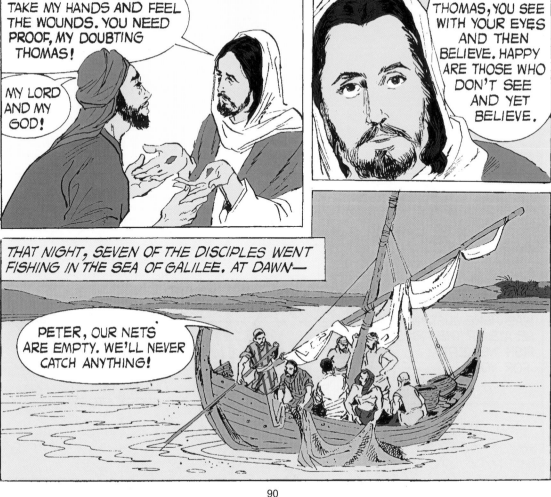

THAT NIGHT, SEVEN OF THE DISCIPLES WENT FISHING IN THE SEA OF GALILEE. AT DAWN—

PETER, OUR NETS ARE EMPTY. WE'LL NEVER CATCH ANYTHING!

AFTER THE MEAL—

PETER, DO YOU LOVE ME?

YES, LORD, YOU KNOW I LOVE YOU!

THEN LOOK AFTER MY FOLLOWERS AS A SHEPHERD LOOKS AFTER HIS SHEEP.

THEN THEY WENT TO THE MOUNT OF OLIVES, NEAR JERUSALEM, WHERE OTHER DISCIPLES JOINED THEM.

GO OUT INTO THE WHOLE WORLD. PREACH MY MESSAGE TO ALL NATIONS.

I WILL BE WITH YOU TILL THE END OF TIME.

BEFORE THEIR EYES, JESUS WAS TAKEN UP TO HEAVEN. HIS HUMAN NATURE WAS GLORIFIED. THE SON HAD COMPLETED HIS TASK AND RETURNED TO THE FATHER.

THAT NIGHT, THE ELEVEN DISCIPLES MET IN JERUSALEM TO PRAY TOGETHER. MARY, THE MOTHER OF JESUS, AND OTHERS WERE ALSO PRESENT.

COME, HOLY SPIRIT, AND FILL OUR HEARTS.

SEND YOUR SPIRIT, LORD.

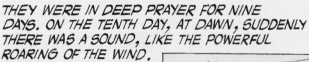

THEY WERE IN DEEP PRAYER FOR NINE DAYS. ON THE TENTH DAY, AT DAWN, SUDDENLY THERE WAS A SOUND, LIKE THE POWERFUL ROARING OF THE WIND.

THE SPIRIT OF THE LORD HAS COME UPON US!

AND THEY SAW SOMETHING LIKE TONGUES OF FIRE. ALL THOSE PRESENT WERE FILLED WITH THE HOLY SPIRIT.

GLORY!

GLORY BE TO GOD!

THE STRANGE HAPPENINGS ATTRACTED THE PEOPLE OF JERUSALEM—

WHAT'S HAPPENING UP THERE?

I CAN HEAR THEM SPEAKING IN STRANGE LANGUAGES!

IS THE HOUSE ON FIRE?

SOME PEOPLE FOUND IT VERY FUNNY.

HA! HA! THOSE MEN HAVE BEEN DRINKING TOO MUCH WINE!

HA! HA!

PETER, THE LEADER OF THE DISCIPLES CAME OUT.

MEN OF ISRAEL, LISTEN TO ME CAREFULLY! WHAT YOU SEE AND HEAR IS THE POWER OF GOD'S HOLY SPIRIT SENT TO US BY JESUS YOU PUT JESUS CHRIST TO DEATH BUT GOD HAS GIVEN HIM VICTORY OVER SIN AND DEATH!

HEARING THE BOLD BUT TRUE WORDS OF PETER, THE PEOPLE WERE VERY TOUCHED.

WHAT SHOULD WE DO, BROTHERS?

SHOW US THE WAY.

CHANGE YOUR LIVES! THEN YOU, TOO, WILL RECEIVE THE PEACE AND POWER OF GOD'S HOLY SPIRIT!

FROM THAT DAY ONWARDS, CHRISTIANITY* KEPT SPREADING ALL OVER THE WORLD. JESUS CHRIST STILL ATTRACTS MILLIONS OF PEOPLE TODAY.

*THESE PEOPLE WERE LATER CALLED CHRISTIANS, i.e. FOLLOWERS OF CHRIST